Jedi Emergency

The galaxy is yours.
Be a part of

#1 Search for the Lost Jedi
#2 The Bartokk Assassins
#3 The Fury of Darth Maul
#4 Jedi Emergency

. . . and more to come!

#4

Jedi Emergency

Ryder Windham

SCHOLASTIC INC.

New York Toronto London Auckland Sydney
Mexico City New Delhi Hong Kong

ISBN 0-439-10141-7

12 11 10 9 8 7 6 5 4 3 2 1   9/9 0 1 2 3 4/0

Printed in the U.S.A.
First Scholastic printing, December 1999

INTRODUCTION

After the Jedi Master Qui-Gon Jinn and his Padawan Learner Obi-Wan Kenobi battled reprogrammed droids and Bartokk assassins on the planet Esseles, they traveled with Bama Vook and the droid Leeper to the ice planet Rhinnal. The Jedi Knights Noro Zak and Vel Ardox had transported the wounded Jedi Master Adi Gallia to the Jedi Chapter House on Rhinnal, and Qui-Gon wanted to check on Adi's condition. The good news was that Adi Gallia had almost fully recovered. The bad news was that a magnetic storm left the Jedi temporarily stranded on Rhinnal, and prevented them from pursuing a Bartokk freighter to the Corulag system.

At this time in history, the Jedi believed the evil Sith had been extinct for over a thousand years. In truth, the dark order had survived in secrecy, and two Sith Lords were very much alive on the planet Coruscant.

After the Sith Lord Darth Sidious was informed that fifty Trade Federation droid starfighters had been stolen by Bartokks from an Esseles factory, he sent his apprentice Darth Maul to hunt down the thieves and retrieve the starfighters. During his pursuit of the Bartokks, Darth Maul learned that twenty-five droid starfighters had already been destroyed by Jedi Knights.

Maul also learned the Bartokks had been hired by Groodo the Hutt, the father of young Boonda. Groodo had been angered because the Trade Federation had refused to pay him for building the droid starfighters' prototype hyperdrive engine, and he was further enraged when Corulag Academy rejected Boonda's application. Desiring revenge, Boonda had contracted the Bartokks to steal the Trade Federation starfighters and use them to attack the Academy.

Because of Darth Maul, Groodo's plan failed. The ruthless Maul destroyed an entire fifteen-member Bartokk hive, blew up Groodo's cruiser, and returned the remaining twenty-five starfighters to an area controlled by the Trade Federation. Groodo and Boonda survived the assault, and their escape pod landed in the dense forest outside of Corulag's capital city Curamelle.

Meanwhile, on Rhinnal, Qui-Gon was informed that the missing twenty-five droid starfighters had not reached Corulag. Qui-Gon and Obi-Wan were preparing to leave Rhinnal when Qui-Gon received a message from Jedi Master Yoda at the Jedi Temple on Coruscant. Despite the fact that the Bartokks had failed their mission, Yoda urged Qui-Gon and the other Jedi to meet him at Corulag Academy. Yoda did not offer any explanations, but Qui-Gon knew it had to be a matter of great importance.

As the Jedi and their allies raced for Corulag, they were unaware that a vengeful Groodo was hatching a final, desperate plan.

CHAPTER ONE

Thirty-four kilometers southwest of the city Curamelle on the planet Corulag, the young Hutt named Boonda lay slumped against the outside of the escape pod. It had only been about fifteen minutes since the pod had ejected from Groodo the Hutt's lavish cruiser and safely delivered both Hutts to the Corulag forest. Since the cruiser had been blasted to bits, Boonda's thoughts turned to a more immediate concern: his growling stomach.

Just before the cruiser's destruction, Boonda had eaten seven bowls of lizards. He usually ate twelve bowls of lizards for lunch, so he was still quite hungry. Boonda wanted to break into the pod's emergency food provisions, but he didn't want to interrupt his father, Groodo, who was inside the pod, talking on the comm unit. With nothing better to do, Boonda pressed the side of his wide head against the pod and listened to his father's conversation.

"Now, listen here, you bug-eyed swindler," Groodo said, speaking to someone on the other side of the galaxy. "You Bartokks failed to steal the starfighters, and your error has cost me my starcruiser. The Trade Federation doesn't interest me anymore, but I've spent a small fortune on your Assassins Guild, and I demand results! You assured me that Corulag Academy would be blown sky-high. Unless you wipe out the Academy, I'll want all my money back!"

Having heard enough, Boonda pulled his head away from the pod. He couldn't believe his father had gotten so worked up over Corulag Academy's refusal to let Boonda enter the Science Service.

Boonda saw something out of the corner of one of his large eyes. It was a beautiful multicolored six-winged insect. It flew past Boonda's head, then stopped and hovered near the escape pod. The insect had never seen a Hutt before, and it flew back for a closer inspection. It neared Boonda's face, and the Hutt smiled as he admired the small creature's wings. He opened his wide mouth and unleashed his tongue, lashing out and snagging the insect in midair. His sticky tongue darted back into his mouth with a loud smacking sound, and he felt the insect squirm in his mouth.

"Yum," said Boonda.

Far from Corulag, in a remote hideout on an uncharted planet near the Corporate Sector of space, a lean-muscled insectoid alien switched off the comm unit mounted in the wall of her communications bunker. The alien was a Bartokk Queen, and the leader of the Bartokk chapter of the Assassins Guild. She had just completed a long-distance conversation with Groodo the Hutt, and the exchange had left her seething with anger.

The Bartokk Queen was in charge of directing the action for every Bartokk assassin squad in the galaxy. She had believed that two Bartokk hives were more than enough to handle the job for Groodo. Despite her confidence, both hives had been eliminated.

The Bartokk Queen exited the bunker and walked quickly to the training room. It was a wide chamber with a single round window at the center of the high, domed ceiling. Within the room, fifteen Bartokks were practicing their fighting skills against skeletal training droids. The Bartokk Queen pressed a yellow button on the wall and the training droids all stopped in their tracks. The fifteen insectoid assassins lay down their weapons and turned their bulbous, multifaceted eyes to face their leader.

An unknown enemy has jeopardized the Corulag assignment, the Queen telepathically communicated to her hive. *Furthermore, thirty brothers from our Guild have been slain. We will have our vengeance, but first we must honor our contract with Groodo and complete the assignment. It is likely that Corulag Academy is now prepared for an attack, so we must use extreme stealth. Prepare to leave for Corulag at once!*

CHAPTER TWO

It was snowing on Rhinnal when the starships *Radiant VII* and *Metron Burner* rose up and away from the circular landing bay that bordered the Jedi chapter house. The diplomatic cruiser *Radiant VII* carried Jedi Master Adi Gallia and the Jedi Knights Vel Ardox and Noro Zak. Within the *Metron Burner*'s cockpit, the Jedi Knight Qui-Gon Jinn and his apprentice Obi-Wan Kenobi were strapped into their seats behind the Talz pilot Bama Vook and the droid Leeper.

Leeper's metal fingers tapped away at the *Burner*'s nav computer. "After we make the jump to lightspeed, we should arrive in the Corulag system in thirty-four minutes," Leeper informed the passengers.

Bama turned his hairy head to gaze back at Qui-Gon and joked, "Maybe we should race the *Radiant VII* through hyperspace?"

Qui-Gon replied, "You don't have to prove anything to me, Bama. It's a safe bet your ship would win that race."

The Talz was greatly pleased by Qui-Gon's answer. His four eyes beamed with pride as he returned his attention to the ship's controls.

Qui-Gon looked at Obi-Wan and saw disapproval in his apprentice's expression. "Something on your mind, Padawan?" Qui-Gon asked.

Keeping his voice low so Bama and Leeper would not hear, Obi-Wan said. "I'm grateful to the

Talz and the droid for delivering us to Rhinnal, but they should have been discouraged from taking us to Corulag. We should be traveling with the other Jedi."

Qui-Gon considered Obi-Wan's statement, then asked, "Back on Coruscant, when Mace Windu advised that you shouldn't join me on the mission to Esseles, how did that make you feel?"

Obi-Wan was surprised by his Master's query. "Before you locked me on board the *Radiant VII*, I had every intention of obeying Master Windu."

"I'm sure you did, Padawan. But you still haven't answered my question."

"All right, then," Obi-Wan said. "I admit, I was disappointed when Master Windu said I should remain on Coruscant."

"Why?"

"Because Adi Gallia was in trouble and I wanted to help."

Qui-Gon nodded. "There you have it. You wanted to *help*. Now, tell me. Should the Jedi have a monopoly on the desire to help others?"

"Of course not," Obi-Wan said. "But that's not the point. We don't even know why Master Yoda has asked us to meet him on Corulag. We could be endangering Bama and Leeper."

"I think they know the risks," Qui-Gon replied. "Perhaps you should be more concerned with what

Yoda is going to do when he sees you with me. After all, he was in the Council chambers when Mace Windu told you to stay on Coruscant."

Obi-Wan was flabbergasted. "But you practically abducted me to Esseles!"

Keeping his voice calm, Qui-Gon answered, "You need not be defensive, Obi-Wan." Qui-Gon closed his eyes and assumed a restful position, then said, "I accept full responsibility for you. If Yoda is displeased that you joined me on this mission, he'll deal with me."

Obi-Wan found little comfort in Qui-Gon's words. Yoda was a great teacher who could also be a stern disciplinarian. While Obi-Wan found himself almost wishing he'd remained on Coruscant, Leeper declared, "Hang on, back there. We're ready to make the jump." Seconds later, the *Metron Burner* and *Radiant VII* blasted into hyperspace.

A fifty-meter-long SoroSuub space yacht tore out of hyperspace and entered the Corulag system. The sleek new yacht had been built as a pleasure craft, and it featured many luxurious details. Twin engine pods extended from the yacht's main hull, and retractable viewports lined both the port and starboard sides. The yacht had been commissioned for a wealthy Trandoshan, but the owner was not present. Instead, the yacht carried the Bartokk Queen, fifteen Bartokks, and six remote-control-operated X10-D draft droids.

The Bartokks had stolen both the space yacht and the droids from a starship factory on the planet Sullust. The yacht had been selected for two reasons: The Bartokks wanted to avoid identification on Corulag, and they wanted a vessel with a powerful hyperdrive engine in case they needed to make a quick getaway. Since the yacht wasn't a combat vessel, the Bartokks hoped it wouldn't attract any unwanted attention.

Six Bartokks were stationed on the yacht's main deck to test the X10-D droids. Each Bartokk operated a handheld transmitter that signaled instructions to a single droid. Standing just over three meters tall, X10-Ds were twice the height of 3PO protocol droids. Unlike protocol droids, X10-Ds could only be operated by remote-control signals. The Trandoshans — reptilian aliens lacking dexterous hands and nimble fingers — had designed and manufactured the X10-Ds for loading freight at interstellar spaceports. The droids were equipped with powerful arms, massive conical torsos, infrared photoreceptors, and treaded roller feet. The six X10-Ds appeared in every way ordinary as they were instructed to walk across the yacht's main deck.

But not all of the droids were ordinary. Immediately after stealing the X10-Ds, the Bartokks had opened the torsos of a select number of droids and installed compact plasma bombs. Each bomb carried enough firepower to level a small city.

The Bartokks' plan was simple. While they used the non-modified X10-Ds as scouts and decoys, the bomb-carrying droids would be maneuvered to strategic locations within the Academy's Science Service tower. After the lethal droids were in position, the Bartokks would escape Corulag and trigger the plasma bombs.

The Bartokk Queen stood on the yacht's bridge and gazed through a viewport at Corulag. The Queen did not know what had gone wrong with the plan to attack the Academy, and she was still furious about the loss of thirty assassins and the Trade Federation droid starfighters. Granted, Groodo the Hutt had said he no longer cared to seek revenge on the Trade Federation, but the fact remained the Bartokks had failed.

The Queen would not allow that to happen again.

The stolen space yacht slipped into orbit around Corulag. Suddenly, a warning light flashed above the sensor console on the bridge, prompting the Queen to glance at the main sensor screen. Two starships had just materialized from hyperspace less than a kilometer away. One ship was a Corellian freighter and the other was a Republic diplomatic cruiser. Since neither ship appeared to pose any threat, the Queen dismissed them as unimportant.

Prepare to land and deploy the droids, the Queen communicated to her minions. *After the droids are in position, we will set their detonation timers and leave Corulag.* Clicking her facial mandibles, the Queen added, *In two hours, the Academy will be nothing but radioactive cinders.*

CHAPTER THREE

Seconds after the *Radiant VII* and *Metron Burner* exited hyperspace and entered the Corulag System, the droid Leeper's keen photoreceptors spotted a distant ship in Corulag's orbit. Leeper craned his head to get a better view of the ship through the *Burner*'s cockpit canopy.

"There's a SoroSuub space yacht a kilometer off our starboard side," Leeper commented to Bama, Qui-Gon, and Obi-Wan. "It looks like the newest model."

Bama threw a glance over his shoulder to Qui-Gon and Obi-Wan, then said, "You'll have to forgive Leeper. Identifying obscure starships is something of a hobby for him."

Leeper turned to Bama and said in a slightly petulant tone, "I only mentioned it because SoroSuub's newest model isn't yet commercially available. That ship should still be in the factory on Sullust."

"We'd better run an identification check on it," Bama said.

Leeper trained the *Burner*'s sensors on the yacht to identify its ownership and origin. "According to the ID profile, the yacht's owned by a trader named Ausec Grogle of Trandosha."

"Maybe the manufacturer is taking it for a test flight," Obi-Wan muttered.

"Perhaps," Qui-Gon said as the distant yacht angled toward Corulag. "But we're an awfully long way from Sullust and Trandosha . . ."

Qui-Gon was interrupted by a quick series of beeps from the *Burner*'s communications console, followed by the voice of Adi Gallia. "*Radiant VII* to *Metron Burner*. The Academy Spaceport reports they haven't sighted any Bartokk freighters. We're cleared for landing in Docking Bay 39-G. Master Yoda has already arrived, and he's expecting us."

"Well, he's expecting *most* of us anyway," Qui-Gon answered as he looked at his Padawan. Obi-Wan grimaced.

"One more thing," Adi Gallia added. "The mission to Corulag is more important than I'd imagined. Yoda came with Mace Windu."

Hearing this information, Obi-Wan's face went red. There was no longer any doubt in his mind that he should have stayed on Coruscant as Mace Windu had instructed. Obi-Wan had already been uneasy about confronting Yoda, but the prospect of also facing Mace Windu filled him with something resembling dread. He looked at Qui-Gon and said, "I don't suppose you'll let me off here?"

Qui-Gon seemed to ignore Obi-Wan's question as he ordered, "Take us down, Bama."

While the *Metron Burner* followed the *Radiant VII* in a descent to Corulag, Leeper realized he couldn't shake thoughts of the SoroSuub space yacht from his positronic brain. If he were an organic creature, he might have confessed he had a bad feeling about that yacht. But because he was a modest droid, Leeper tended to keep his feelings to himself.

Leeper scanned the area with his photoreceptors for one more glimpse of the space yacht.

It had already vanished from view.

Among the other planets in the Darpa and Bormea Sector, Corulag had long been considered insignificant. Unlike Esseles and Ralltiir, Corulag did not have centers for high-tech research or intergalactically famous banks. Its terrain would never match the agricultural capacity of Chandrila or the icy beauty of Rhinnal. Corulag's climate was more hospitable than the dry planet Brentaal, but then Brentaal had the advantage of being at the strategic intersection of both the Perlemian Trade Route and the Hydian Way.

Everything changed for Corulag when the Academy began scouting for a planet on which to build a new institute. For years, the Academy had to turn away applicants from the planet Raithall because they had too many students. Corulag seemed to be the perfect solution. Academy representatives were delighted by Corulag's almost undeveloped quality and its proximity to the popular Brentaal.

They knew they could transform Corulag for the Academy's needs, and rely on Brentaal spacers to spread the word of the new facilities.

Within two decades, Corulag's population had increased over a hundred times, and the planet's face had changed as well. Flat plains had been terraformed into canyons to create obstacle courses for flight training, and the once-small city of Curamelle had become a great metropolis.

It was dusk as the *Radiant VII* and *Metron Burner* descended to Academy Spaceport. The spaceport was a vast network of open-roofed hexagonal structures interlinked over twelve square kilometers at the outskirts of Curamelle. From the night sky above, the spaceport resembled a gigantic illuminated hive.

Docking Bay 39-G had ample room to contain two medium-sized starships. The *Radiant VII* was the first to land, followed by the *Metron Burner*. Adi Gallia, Vel Ardox, and Noro Zak disembarked the *Radiant VII*, and walked to the wide garage doorway that led out of the docking bay. There, a droid-chauffeured repulsorlift transport hovered in the air behind the welcoming party of Mace Windu and Yoda.

Qui-Gon stepped out of the *Burner* and down the landing ramp to the tarmac. He was followed by the hesitant Obi-Wan, who had some difficulty returning the gaze of Mace Windu and Yoda. Adi

Gallia was speaking to Mace Windu and Yoda, but all three Jedi Council members looked directly at Obi-Wan.

Qui-Gon strode directly to the small group of Jedi Masters and said, "I accept full responsibility for taking Obi-Wan to Esseles and . . ."

"No, Master Qui-Gon," Obi-Wan boldly interjected. Turning to face Yoda and Mace Windu, he declared, "The responsibility is mine. I left Coruscant with Qui-Gon Jinn because I wanted to help. I'm sorry I disobeyed you, Master Windu."

Mace Windu's unblinking eyes did not waver as he replied, "From what Adi Gallia has just told me, it was fortunate you stayed at your Master's side. According to her, if you had not pursued the Bartokk freighter from Esseles, at least twenty-five droid starfighters might have reached Corulag Academy."

Obi-Wan was speechless. Filled with admiration and gratitude, he looked to Adi Gallia and bowed his head.

Yoda sighed. "The time for reprimands, this is not. Most serious is our presence here. Reports we have received of an infant on Corulag. Told we are, she is strong with the Force."

Mace Windu nodded. "If the reports are true, it is our duty to bring her to the Temple on Coruscant."

Qui-Gon looked from Mace Windu to Yoda, then

stated, "But someone has protested the child being delivered to the Temple. Otherwise, neither of you would be here."

"You are correct, Qui-Gon," Mace Windu acknowledged. "The Academy's Chief Scientist discovered the infant's high level of midi-chlorians while running a test in the Science Service nursery. The Chief Scientist notified the Jedi Council, but now insists the girl should remain at the Science Service tower for further study."

"And already six months old, the infant is! If to be a Jedi is her destiny, remain on Corulag she cannot," Yoda said.

"So we're here to persuade the scientist to release the child?" Qui-Gon assessed.

Yoda's tapered ears bent back as he nodded. "Strong are the Jedi, but rare are we too. At the Temple, the girl must be raised, or else lost to us she is."

Just then, Mace Windu saw Bama Vook and Leeper emerge from the *Metron Burner* and walk down the landing ramp. "Acquaintances of yours, Qui-Gon?" asked the Senior Jedi Master.

"Friends," Qui-Gon answered, "and I'd like to invite them to accompany us to the Science Service tower."

"Always friends, we can use," Yoda said as he turned to the repulsorlift transport. "Never enough can we have."

Obi-Wan wasn't certain, but he thought there was a sense of sadness in Yoda's tone.

Night had fallen, and stars sparkled like diamonds in Corulag's clear sky. The Academy's Science Service tower was a four-sided pyramidal skyscraper of plastoid and transparisteel. The tower's first-floor base encompassed six city blocks, and its uppermost point was two hundred stories high. Bordered by older campus buildings, the tower dominated the skyline like an artificial mountain.

The northwest corner of the tower's seventh floor contained administrative offices and a large nursery for the children of Science Service scholars and employees. Managed by small Model E baby-sitting droids, the nursery featured a central indoor playground and a gyroscopic carousel. The carousel was decorated with molded seats shaped like smiling alien beasts, all of which rotated in a dizzying manner that delighted the young riders.

Mace Windu, Yoda, and Adi Gallia stepped out of a seventh-floor conference room and into a brightly lit main lobby. They walked past a lift tube checkpoint where a security droid prevented unauthorized visitors from entering Level 7.

Just off the lobby, a dozen small droids played with a group of thirty toddlers in the playground. As the three Jedi Masters walked by the playground, the sight of Yoda nearly caused two excited youngsters to tumble from their repulsorlift scooters. The children had no idea of Yoda's great power, but they were fascinated by his short, elderly form.

The three Jedi Masters found the others waiting near a wide floor-to-ceiling picture window that looked out over the roofs of the tower's neighboring buildings.

As Yoda, Mace Windu, and Adi Gallia approached, Qui-Gon knew from their grave expressions that the conference with the Chief Scientist had not gone well.

"What happened?" Qui-Gon asked.

"The situation is complicated," Mace Windu answered. "The Force-sensitive infant's name is Teela Panjarra. Her parents were Academy scholars who perished in an accident during a dig. According to Chief Scientist Frexton, Teela is now in a private nursery here at the tower."

Adi Gallia added, "Frexton said he will consider the girl's release to the Jedi Temple, but not until the Academy has conducted a series of physical and neurological tests."

In a hushed tone, Yoda said, "Lying, Frexton is. More extreme tests in mind, we sense he has."

"Then we must stop him," Qui-Gon proclaimed. "Even if Teela Panjarra is Force-sensitive, she is still a child. The Academy is treating her like a lab experiment."

Yoda shook his head. "Unfortunately, authorized the Academy is."

"It seems the Chief Scientist has some influential friends in the Galactic Senate," Adi Gallia said. "The Academy won't even allow us to see Teela. It's doubtful the Senate will hear our appeal before she is too old to enter the Temple."

"Where is Frexton now?" Qui-Gon asked.

"Left our meeting in a hurry, did he," Yoda answered. "Went to see the Panjarra child, we imagine."

As the Jedi pondered their next move, Leeper sighted two droids entering Level 7 from the emergency stairwell doorway. In unison, they crossed the lobby to the security checkpoint. Leeper quickly recognized the pair as X10-D draft droids, remote-control-operated units designed for the reptilian Trandoshans. As soon as Leeper saw the X10-Ds, his processors began to overheat. He turned his metal head to Qui-Gon and said, "Excuse me, sir, but I believe there's something you should know."

"What is it?" Qui-Gon asked.

"The two droids near the security checkpoint are X10-Ds."

Bama Vook scowled and whacked Leeper in the shoulder. Speaking through his vocabulator, the Talz berated, "Knock it off, Leeper. These Jedi are about as interested in your knowledge of droids as they are in your ability to recognize starships."

"It's okay, Bama," Qui-Gon spoke calmly. "Is there something wrong with the droids, Leeper?"

"X10-Ds can only be controlled by a remote signal," Leeper said as he scanned the lobby and the nearby indoor playground. "I see children and Model E baby-sitting droids, but there isn't any sign of the X10-Ds' operators. X10-D draft droids have a control radius of four hundred meters, so the operators might be outside the building, or on another floor. What's most bothersome is that X10-Ds are manufactured to perform maintenance work and freight-loading for Trandoshans."

"Trandoshans?" Qui-Gon said, making the connection immediately. "You think those two droids have something to do with the space yacht we saw, the one that was built for the Trandoshan trader?"

"It seems highly likely, sir. But as you said, we're a long way from Trandosha."

"What's this all about, Master?" Obi-Wan asked.

"Keep your eyes on the droids by the checkpoint, Obi-Wan," Qui-Gon said as he looked out the picture window, searching the surrounding buildings for any suspicious activity. Although it was night, the city lights illuminated the rooftops, and Qui-Gon did not have any difficulty spotting the mysterious SoroSuub space yacht. It was parked on a roof across the street from the Science Service tower, partially obscured by a conical ventilation chimney. Qui-Gon's attention was diverted by two insectoid shadows that shifted across the surface of the chimney itself.

"Bartokks," Qui-Gon uttered, almost in disbelief.

A loud crash sounded at the other end of the lobby. Qui-Gon and the others turned to see the Academy security droid lying sprawled on the floor near the lift tube. Near the checkpoint, a frightened child cried out, then ran to the protective arms of a Model E unit. The two X10-Ds jumped away from the fallen security droid and entered the lift tube.

The alert Obi-Wan raced to the security checkpoint. But before Obi-Wan could reach the X10-Ds, the lift tube doors sealed with a hiss.

Obi-Wan pressed the lift control panel. "The lift won't return," he said in frustration. "The controls are jammed."

"Would someone please explain what's going on?" Mace Windu asked as he and the others ran to the checkpoint.

"It's the Bartokks," Qui-Gon replied. "They came to Corulag on a stolen space yacht and they're using remote-controlled droids to carry out their assignment, just as they did at the factory on Esseles."

If the statement had been made by anyone else, Mace Windu and Yoda would have questioned its veracity. But they knew Qui-Gon well enough to trust his judgment.

"Most deadly are the Bartokks," Yoda said as he glanced back at the window. "At least fifteen of them, there always are."

"And they may be using as many X10-Ds," Obi-Wan added.

"Do you have any idea who might be the Bartokks' target?" Vel Ardox asked.

"No," Qui-Gon answered. "All we know is the Bartokks intended to bring the Trade Federation droid starfighters to Corulag. Since that effort failed, they seem to be trying a different plan."

Leeper propped the fallen Academy security droid up to a seated position against the checkpoint kiosk and asked, "Are you okay?"

"My legs are damaged," the security droid answered. "I tried to prevent the X10-Ds from entering the lift." The droid raised a hand to his broadband antennae. "I'm transmitting to other security droids . . . evacuate all cadets from building. Stop X10-Ds. Bomb threat."

"What do you mean, *bomb threat*?" Leeper asked.

The security droid pointed to the checkpoint computer console. "Security X-ray sensors indicated one of the X10-Ds contained a concealed plasma bomb."

"A plasma bomb?" echoed an alarmed Noro Zak. "That could level an entire quadrant of Curamelle."

"The Bartokks might be attempting to plant the bomb in the tower," Qui-Gon surmised. He ran back to the high window and peered down at the building across the street. The SoroSuub space yacht remained parked behind a broad chimney, but the two Bartokks were not in view. "No sign of the assassins, but their ship is still there. Since the Bartokks have taken the precaution of using the droids, I doubt they're on a suicide mission. They must be planning to make a getaway so they won't be killed when they detonate the plasma bomb."

Suddenly, the lights went off and the entire corridor was thrown into darkness. A number of smaller children began to whimper, and Adi Gallia gently urged them to remain calm.

The disabled security droid rattled against the kiosk. "I managed to transmit the evacuation order, but something is jamming the security communications system."

"The X10-Ds or the Bartokks must have severed a power terminal," Obi-Wan commented.

"An obstacle, the darkness is not," Yoda professed. "Many lives at stake here, there are. Save all the children. Stop the Bartokks and their droids, we must!"

A creaking sound caused the Jedi and their allies to look in the direction of the emergency stairwell. Standing in the stairwell's pitch-black doorway, two new droids were illuminated by the lights of their own infrared photoreceptors.

Both droids were X10-Ds.

At this point, you must decide whether to continue reading this adventure, or to play your own adventure in the Star Wars Adventures *Jedi Emergency* Game Book.

To play your own adventure, turn to the first page of the Game Book and follow the directions you find there.

To continue reading this Jedi adventure, turn the page!

CHAPTER FOUR

The two X10-Ds advanced toward the central indoor playground. Their infrared photoreceptors glowed with menace in the gloomy lobby.

"Those droids aren't authorized to be on this level!" said the damaged security droid, unable to move.

Yoda slipped away from the other Jedi and drew close to the X10-Ds. The Jedi Master knew the Bartokks might be using optical gear to allow themselves to see whatever was within visual range of the remote-controlled X10-Ds' photoreceptors. Yoda was determined not to allow the X10-Ds to harm anyone in the nursery, but he also didn't want to alert the Bartokks to the Jedi presence within the Science Service tower. Instead of openly attacking the X10-Ds, Yoda decided to make the Bartokks think the X10-Ds had an accident.

Yoda moved to the nearest X10-D and extended his gImer stick cane under its rising foot. The droid stumbled and crashed into the other X10-D. With both droids thrown off balance, Yoda reached for his lightsaber and thumbed the activator. As the X10-Ds fell, the lightsaber's glowing blade disabled both droids.

The other Jedi were not surprised by Yoda's action. Despite Yoda's age, they all knew him to be a resourceful fighter. Bama Vook and Leeper, however, were amazed by Yoda's victory over the two draft droids. If they hadn't seen it with their own eyes, they would have had difficulty imagining that Yoda could move with such power.

While the X10-Ds' heads rolled down the corridor floor, Yoda stepped cautiously between the two fallen droids and reached to their armored chest panels. Taking great care, he slid both panels back.

The X10-D on his left contained a plasma bomb.

Qui-Gon bent down beside Yoda and said, "The Bartokks always have a backup plan, so it makes sense that they'd have more than one bomb. They won't dare to trigger the bombs until they're safely away from the city. But now that these two X10-Ds are down, the Bartokks who were controlling them might come looking for them here."

"All children and adults must be removed from the building at once," Adi Gallia stated.

Yoda turned to his allies and proclaimed, "To safety, you will take them. Deactivate the bomb, I will. And find Teela Panjarra."

"Obi-Wan and I can search for the girl, Master Yoda," Qui-Gon suggested.

"Guard and protect these young ones, you will," Yoda said, gesturing to the children in the nursery. "My responsibility, Teela Panjarra is. Knew her parents, I did. Friends we were. Go now, you will."

Qui-Gon and Adi Gallia exchanged concerned glances, then looked to Mace Windu. The senior

Jedi Master appeared unfazed by Yoda's words. "We will see you soon, old friend," he said. "May the Force be with you."

The assembled Jedi, Bama, Leeper, and the Model E units quickly rounded up the children and escorted them to the emergency stairwell, leaving Yoda to examine the plasma bomb. Shaped like a geodesic sphere, the compact bomb was magnetically clamped within the X10-D's chest cavity. A primitive radio transmitter was affixed to the trigger mechanism. Yoda glanced around the indoor playground and noticed a child's sculpture resting on a nearby table.

The Jedi Master went to the table and pried a piece from the child's statue. He wedged it over the plasma bomb's trigger mechanism, preventing the Bartokks from activating the bomb by remote.

With his small, green fingers, Yoda removed the bomb from the droid's torso. Even though the bomb was deactivated, Yoda knew it had to be destroyed. If the Bartokks recovered the bomb intact, they would most certainly attempt to reset it.

And Yoda had a feeling the Bartokks would come soon.

"Good work," praised the damaged Academy security droid, still propped up against the checkpoint kiosk. "Sorry I wasn't any help."

"Here," Yoda said to the droid as he handed him the plasma bomb. "Disassemble this, you can."

As the security droid took the bomb, Yoda heard a hissing sound from the doorway to the emergency stairwell. He turned just in time to see the shadowy forms of two Bartokk assassins slip out of the doorway. The Bartokks dropped their X10-D remote-control devices and leaped at Yoda from across the lobby. Both Bartokks wielded deadly vibro-axes.

Although Yoda was not violent by nature, he realized there wasn't any use in negotiating with the Bartokks. They were cold-blooded killers who would stop at nothing to destroy anyone they perceived as an enemy. Furthermore, they saw the plasma bomb in the security droid's hands. Yoda would not allow the Bartokks to get their claws on the bomb.

Yoda raised one hand and the two Bartokks appeared to slam into an invisible wall. The Jedi Master flung his hand back, and the insectoids launched straight up at the high ceiling. Their bulbous heads crashed into the ceiling, then both figures fell back to the corridor floor.

The Bartokks had underestimated the power of the Force.

The two assassins lay motionless on the floor near the fallen X10-D draft droids. Yoda realized there might be more Bartokks or X10-Ds in the emergency stairwell, so he removed his comlink from his belt and contacted Qui-Gon. "Attacked from the emergency stairwell by two Bartokks, I was. Defeated the two are, but watch for more."

"Thanks for the warning," Qui-Gon replied. "The children and Academy cadets are out of the tower, but we haven't seen Chief Scientist Frexton or any sign of Teela Panjarra. It's possible they're both still inside the —"

A loud burst of static came from Yoda's comlink. Something was interfering with his signal. Yoda suspected the Bartokks were jamming transmissions from the tower.

He was on his own.

CHAPTER FIVE

"What's happening?" asked the damaged security droid.

"With the communications frequencies the Bartokks are interfering, I think," Yoda replied. "Comlinks the Bartokks need not. Communicate telepathically, they do." He pointed to the fallen assassins and added, "If warned their hive these two did about what happened here, already on their way more Bartokks may be."

"I'm afraid I'm not in much condition to defend Level seven anymore," admitted the security droid, looking at his useless legs. He set to the task of taking apart the plasma bomb.

Yoda's thoughts turned to Teela Panjarra. According to Chief Scientist Frexton, the Force-sensitive six-month-old child was in a private nursery within the Science Service tower. There were still two X10-D draft droids in the tower, one of which was carrying a plasma bomb.

While the damaged Academy security droid disassembled the first bomb, Yoda studied the checkpoint's deactivated computer console. He suspected either the X10-Ds or the Bartokks were responsible for severing a power terminal and causing both the lobby to black out and the computer to shut down. Because of the darkness, it was difficult to see the console.

Yoda smacked his lips. "If operational this computer is, learn we might the location of the one named Teela Panjarra."

"Teela Panjarra?" the droid repeated in surprise. "Why, she's being held in a research laboratory on Level fifty-eight."

Yoda's eyes went wide. The girl was in a research lab! Yoda's suspicions were confirmed: the Academy's Chief Scientist was not to be trusted.

"To Level fifty-eight, I must go," Yoda said. He checked the lift tube near the security checkpoint, and found the sliding doors were still tightly sealed. The controls required extensive repairs.

Once again, Yoda drew and activated his lightsaber. With only the slightest turn of his gnarled wrist, Yoda plunged the lightsaber's blade through the doors and carved out a large circle. He tapped at the center of the circle and it fell away into the shaft, leaving a wide hole in the lift tube doors.

Yoda deactivated his lightsaber and stared into the lift tube shaft. The lift itself was gone, having ferried the first two X10-Ds to another level within the Science Service tower. Yoda didn't know whether the two X10-Ds had gone up or down, but he knew his own destination was Level 58.

Above the security kiosk, an air vent rattled on the ceiling. Suddenly, the heavy vent cover swung out on its hinges and two Bartokks plunged down from inside. Just as Yoda had suspected, more Bartokks had been alerted by their fallen comrades.

Both Bartokks carried cryogen whips, capable of causing a near-explosive chemical reaction when the super-cold tip of the lash struck an object. The Bartokks landed next to the damaged security droid. Before the droid could move, the Bartokks brought their cryogen whips down on him. A stunning blast and loud crack sounded as the whips struck, and the helpless droid was instantly reduced to frozen metal.

It was fortunate that the brave security droid had disassembled the plasma bomb. Both the security droid and the bomb's separate components were transformed into useless bits of ice-cold scrap.

Yoda remained standing near the open lift tube shaft when the Bartokks turned away from the security droid and jumped at him. The elderly Jedi Master ducked, and one of the Bartokks sailed over his back and tumbled through the open lift tube doorway. Yoda kept his eyes on the Bartokk who had stopped short of the open door, and heard the other Bartokk crash down through the lift tube shaft. Even though Bartokks had exoskeletal body armor, it was a certainty that the assassin would not survive the drop to the Science Service's subbasement levels.

The remaining Bartokk raised his whip, preparing to strike Yoda. Again, Yoda's lightsaber flashed. Yoda swung out and high to the right, separating his attacker at the abdomen and removing the claw that gripped the whip. The Bartokk's body parts attempted to regroup. One arm accidentally lashed out with the whip and struck the Bartokk's upper torso, which exploded into icy splinters. Seconds later, the body parts were motionless.

Yoda believed more Bartokks would soon be on their way to Level 7. He looked inside the lift tube shaft, trying to determine whether there was any way for him to reach Level 58. On the inner wall of the shaft, a maintenance ladder offered the possibility for ascent. Yoda glanced back at the nursery and saw a flatboard repulsorlift scooter hovering a few millimeters over the floor. The small scooter was designed for a child, but it looked just about right to Yoda.

Throughout his life, Yoda found that his size often worked to his benefit. Had he been as large as a typical full-grown human, the scooter would not have been able to support his weight. Yoda climbed onto the repulsorlift scooter and gripped the handlebars. He shifted his balance and aimed for the lift tube, then revved the motor.

The scooter passed through the hole in the lift tube doors and rocketed up the shaft. Yoda clung to the handlebars and rapidly counted the passing levels as he ascended through near-total darkness. Within seconds, he reached Level 58 and slowed the scooter down. He gripped the shaft's maintenance ladder and climbed off the scooter, then edged over to an access door. The door was locked, but the locking mechanism was on the inside of the shaft. Yoda's stubby fingers danced over the lock, opening the mechanism within seconds.

Yoda stepped through the access door and entered Level 58. Like the nursery fifty-one floors below, all the lights were off.

An Academy security droid was stationed next to the northeast lift tube. "You are not authorized to enter this level," the security droid stated. "Command received from Level seven . . . all organic life-forms must evacuate the building."

"Came from Level seven, I did," Yoda proclaimed, ignoring the droid's directive. "Here to help, I am. Search, I do, for a six-month-old girl named Teela Panjarra. Held in a research lab on this level, she is."

"Teela Panjarra is in the care of Chief Scientist Frexton," the droid answered. "I will direct you to the nearest exit."

Yoda stood his ground and asked, "On this level the Chief Scientist is, or leave, did he, with the girl?"

The droid quickly reached out to grab Yoda's arm. "Warning . . . You must leave immediately."

The Academy security droid might have been merely following orders, but Yoda sensed the droid was deliberately not answering his questions. Yoda imagined it was possible the droid was acting under direct orders from the duplicitous Chief Scientist.

"An attack on Level seven, there has been," Yoda told the droid. "Needed there, you are."

The droid pulled Yoda by the arm. "You are trespassing. You will leave here at once."

Yoda sighed. "Leave me with no choice, you do." The Jedi Master concentrated on the droid's fingers, and the fingers drew back, releasing Yoda from their grip. Before the droid could process what invisible power could have caused his metal fingers to open, it fell back to the floor.

While the droid tried to raise itself, Yoda proceeded into the lobby. On a wall next to a reception desk, he saw a map that revealed ten different research laboratories on Level 58. Each lab was represented by a color-coded rectangle. Yoda raised his walking stick to tap at each of the rectangles, and a monitor displayed a readout of the respective lab's purpose and contents.

According to the information on the monitor, Teela Panjarra was in the fifth laboratory. Yoda did not see any sign of the infant on the monitor, but he sensed she was indeed there. He moved quietly toward the lab.

Yoda reached the fifth research lab and peered inside the dark chamber. The lab was a long, deep room, dimly illuminated by the city light that seeped through a tinted picture window. Looking outside, Yoda saw starships flying to and from the Academy Spaceport.

Yoda's eyes adjusted to the darkness and he scanned the lab. Electrical equipment was set up on a thick plastoid table. Hundreds of chemical vials were neatly displayed upon a series of wall-mounted shelves. Below the window he saw a dispersal canister for destroying trash and a portable fusion furnace for power generation.

Suddenly, the silhouette of a tall, slender man wearing a laboratory tunic moved in front of the picture window. The man was transferring something that looked like a bundled sack from a shallow rectangular tray into a medium-sized box. Despite the darkness, Yoda recognized the box as a Live Organism Comfort Conveyor (LOCC), a contraption used to transport small animals during interstellar journeys.

Yoda reached for the emergency glow rod on his belt. As soon as the slender man closed the lid on the LOCC, Yoda activated the glow rod. Instantly,

Chief Scientist Frexton was caught in the rod's bright projected light, and he threw a hand up over his eyes. A small transparent viewport was built into the side of the LOCC, and it revealed that the bundled sack was in fact an infant swaddled in pale gray fabric.

Teela Panjarra was sound asleep.

CHAPTER SIX

The sleeping infant was humanoid. She was so safely nestled within the LOCC that Yoda did not want to disturb her. Keeping his voice calm, Yoda commanded, "Surrender at once, Frexton."

"Security!" Frexton yelped as he squinted into the glow rod's light. "Security! Get here at once!"

"Help you, the security droid cannot," Yoda informed the scientist. "Deceived the Jedi Council, you have. Now, away from the child you will step or . . ."

Before Yoda could complete his sentence, the Chief Scientist drew a concealed blaster from his lab tunic. He raised the blaster fast and prepared to fire at the small Jedi Master.

Yoda threw his glow rod at Frexton's blaster, his arm moving so fast that Frexton never knew what hit him. The blaster was suddenly slammed out of his hands. The room was again cast into darkness.

Frexton cursed as his blaster smashed to the floor, ruined. Yoda was about to reach for the box containing the sleeping Teela Panjarra when he was distracted by movement outside the tinted window. Rising from a lower level, a wide viewport-cleaning drone rolled on magnetic treads up the tower's inclined exterior. On the drone's broad back stood two Bartokk assassins and a pair of X10-D draft droids. With some frustration, Yoda realized it was possible the Bartokks were drawn to the window because of the light from his glow rod.

Both Bartokks held X10-D remote-control devices in their lower set of hands. With their upper limbs, one Bartokk operated the window-washing drone while the other fired a shoulder-mounted Squib battering ram, unleashing a powerful burst of alternating energy pulsations. The transparisteel window shattered.

Frexton ducked behind a cabinet. Some of the transparisteel shrapnel struck the lab's utility wall and punctured a plastoid plumbing hose, causing water to spray out all over the floor. Fortunately, Teela Panjarra was shielded from the shrapnel and water by her protective LOCC.

One of the two Bartokks wore a vocabulator. "Nobody movessss!" he hissed.

As the two Bartokks leaped into the room, the Chief Scientist cowered behind the cabinet. The Bartokk assassins ignored the cringing scientist and focused their attention on the weapons in Yoda's belt.

"Brave warrior, are you, little one?" asked the vocabulator-equipped Bartokk. "We'll sssssee how tough you are."

The two Bartokks adjusted their X10-D remote-control devices, and the X10-D draft droids raised their extendable loader arms and lurched toward Yoda. Water from the punctured plumbing hose had formed a large puddle in the middle of the lab.

Yoda noticed the Bartokks were standing in the puddle.

Yoda jumped on top of the nearby table as he pushed the electrical equipment hard. The equipment crashed into the watery puddle, and sent a massive electric jolt through the two insectoid assassins. A fizzing sound filled the air as the Bartokks appeared to be frozen in their tracks. Without anyone to control them, the X10-Ds ceased their movement. After several seconds, the Bartokks were completely fried. Yoda carefully deactivated the equipment's port from the fusion furnace, and the electric shock ended. The two Bartokks collapsed into the puddle.

The frightened Chief Scientist Frexton whimpered from behind the cabinet. Yoda looked at the LOCC and was amused to see that Teela Panjarra was still fast asleep.

The vocabulator-equipped Bartokk twitched on the wet floor. Still alive, the fiendish assassin looked up at Yoda and hissed. Yoda could see the Bartokk was mortally wounded, and felt something resembling remorse. However, Yoda was confident he had done the right thing. If he had not fought the Bartokks, he and Teela Panjarra might have been their next victims.

Yoda wanted to know the nature of the Bartokks' murderous assignment. With this information, Yoda hoped he would have a better chance of stopping any other bomb-carrying X10-Ds. He gazed into the dying Bartokk's multifaceted eyes and relaxed.

"How many plasma bombs are there?" Yoda asked the Bartokk. "Many more droids you have, hmmm?"

Unable to resist Yoda's power, the Bartokk answered, "Six droids . . . three bombs . . . destroy the Science Service tower . . . that is our assignment." As he uttered the last word, the assassin's bulbous eyes seemed to flex in his insectoid skull.

"Assigned you were, by whom?" Yoda asked, but it was too late. The vile Bartokk's facial mandibles clicked as he exhaled his last foul breath. He was gone.

"Is it true?" asked the frightened Chief Scientist Frexton. "Are those creatures really going to blow up the Academy?"

"Their intention, it is, yes," Yoda replied as he examined the two fallen X10-Ds. Without telling Frexton that one of the three bombs was no longer a concern, Yoda carefully opened the panels on the droids' chests. One of the droids contained a plasma bomb.

Suddenly, two grappling hooks sailed through the open window. Both hooks were tied to climbing cables. The cables were drawn taut and the hooks were secured to the base of the windowsill.

Yoda fixed his eyes on Frexton and whispered, "Move not!" The fearful Frexton ducked back behind the cabinet.

Yoda moved to the window and glanced down. Gripping the lines, two Bartokks pulled themselves up to Level 58 from a balcony below.

The Jedi Master realized how the Bartokks could have known where to look for him. Before the vocabulator-equipped Bartokk died, he had sent a telepathic communication to his comrades.

Yoda sighed.

The trouble was not over yet.

CHAPTER SEVEN

Yoda knew if the two Bartokks reached Level 58, they would do whatever they could to recover their plasma bomb. They wouldn't hesitate to eliminate everyone in the room.

The Jedi Master did not falter. He activated his lightsaber and slashed the climbing cables. The severed cables whipped out of the window, and the Bartokks fell.

The Jedi Master did not enjoy watching the two assassins plummet down the side of the pyramidal tower. But he watched them long enough to make sure they were no longer a threat. Only when he was satisfied that there were two less Bartokks did he look back into the lab.

Yoda hunkered down over the plasma bomb within the X10-D draft droid. While he removed the bomb from the droid's torso, Chief Scientist Frexton made his move. Frexton grabbed the LOCC by its handle and ran through a triangular doorway, carrying Teela Panjarra with him.

Yoda heard Frexton slip through the door and realized he should have subdued the Chief Scientist when he had the chance. Although Frexton had Teela Panjarra, Yoda was compelled to get rid of the plasma bomb before pursuing the scientist. The laboratory was outfitted with the perfect utility for disposal.

Yoda carried the bomb to the waste dispersal canister and raised the canister's lid. He dropped the bomb into the unit, sealed the lid, and activated the contained fusion reactor. The canister hummed, and the plasma bomb disintegrated.

Almost too easy, that was, Yoda thought to himself as he hobbled to the triangular doorway. Yoda meditated and exercised every day, but he knew that age had taken its toll on his body. For a fleeting moment, he wondered if it had been unwise for him to have insisted on rescuing Teela Panjarra. Rescue missions were for Jedi Knights, not elderly Jedi Masters. Still, Yoda moved faster than most beings who were over eight hundred years old.

Yoda reached the doorway only to find it was sealed by a transparent energy field. He realized Frexton must have activated the field as soon as he'd entered the next chamber. Yoda gazed through the invisible field and into the adjoining laboratory. From what he could see, the lab was dedicated to hydroponic research. The lab was filled with water tanks that contained large alien plants. Frexton was at the far end of the lab, carrying the conveyor as he walked toward a lift tube.

Yoda considered using his lightsaber to carve through the wall, but the walls appeared thick and it could take more time than he could afford. Then he remembered the Bartokks' Squib battering ram.

The Jedi Master turned and hobbled back to the fallen Bartokks and picked up the battering ram.

The weapon was larger than Yoda, but he hefted it over his right shoulder and aimed it at the laboratory wall.

Yoda fired. With a single blast, the battering ram punched a broad hole through the thick wall. Yoda dropped the weapon and scrambled into the hydroponics laboratory.

At the other end of the lab, Frexton was standing in front of a lift tube door, waiting for a lift to arrive. He had turned at the sound of the battering ram, and gasped when he saw Yoda.

"You can't have the child!" Frexton shouted, clenching the live organism comfort conveyor tightly against his chest. "My research depends on her. She belongs to the Academy!"

"A piece of property, Teela Panjarra is not," Yoda replied. "Still in great danger, we are. Surrender, you must."

Frexton ignored Yoda's order and ran behind a barrel-shaped transparisteel water tank. The tank contained an immense purple plant. The plant's thick, leaf-covered vines extended out of the top of the tank and brushed the ceiling, then curved out and dangled down to the white-tiled floor.

Yoda pushed his way through the plant's leaves. Moving forward, he felt one of his legs become entangled by the plant's vines. Suddenly, he was yanked off the laboratory floor and raised toward the ceiling.

Yoda was in the grips of the alien plant. As he struggled against the vines, the plant positioned him over the top of the water tank. Inside the tank, under the water's surface, Yoda saw the plant's central stalk widen to reveal a mouth filled with razor-sharp teeth. The stalk rose and broke the water's surface. Yellow foam spilled out of the plant's mouth.

The plant was very, very hungry.

CHAPTER EIGHT

Despite his situation, Yoda did not panic. He knew that survival depended upon maintaining a clear mind.

Yoda concentrated, reaching out to communicate with the plant. The plant's mind was primitive, and its thoughts were only centered around light, warmth, and food. Unable to make any mental connection with the plant, Yoda redirected his concentration on the vines themselves, forcing them to release their grip on him. The plant relented, and Yoda fell to the laboratory floor.

The lift tube doors opened. Frexton ran away from the barrel-shaped tank and jumped into the lift tube.

As Yoda rose from the floor, the lift tube doors began to slide shut. Yoda forced the doors open, but the lift was already descending in the shaft.

Yoda jumped on top of the lift and held on. He had barely caught his breath when the lift came to a sudden, jarring stop. By Yoda's estimate, the lift was somewhere between Levels 35 and 40. He'd thought Frexton might have been attempting to reach Level 1 or one of the Science Service tower's sublevels, so he was surprised that the lift had stopped so soon. Yoda hunkered down on top of the stalled lift and placed his ear over the lift's upper emergency access hatch. He heard the sound of the lift tube doors opening.

Then Chief Scientist Frexton began to scream.

Yoda pulled at the emergency access hatch, but it was jammed. He drew and activated his lightsaber, illuminating the dark lift tube with the weapon's vibrant glow. He sheared the hatch clear off the lift's top, then leaped down through the open hole and into the lift cabin.

From inside the lift cabin, Yoda gazed through the open tube doors to see that he was on Level 32. According to a sign on the wall, this area was devoted to aeronautic research and development.

"Get away from me!" Chief Scientist Frexton yelled from outside the lift.

Yoda stepped out of the lift cabin and the doors slid shut behind him. An antechamber led directly to an aeronautic laboratory, where Academy scientists and engineers developed new repulsorlift systems. Yoda saw a tall, robotic figure standing in the entrance to the lab and almost mistook it for an X10-D before he realized it was just an unmanned bipedal servo-lifter. Like the X10-Ds, servo-lifters were used for moving heavy freight, but they were operated by a pilot instead of remote control. The pilot had already fled. Yoda ducked behind the two-legged loading machine and peered inside the lab.

He saw Frexton cowering against a wall, held at bay by a single X10-D draft droid. Numerous storage bins filled with starship engine parts were also evident, but there wasn't any sign of the comfort conveyor that contained Teela Panjarra. The lab was dimly lit, with much of the area lost to shadows. Yoda scurried up onto the servo-lifter to get a wider view of the room. He didn't see any Bartokks. But he knew they were nearby if they were controlling the X10-D.

"Help!" Frexton shouted as the droid raised a metal claw and prepared to strike.

Yoda switched on the servo-lifter and the robotic freight-loader lurched forward, causing the X10-D to turn. By the time the X10-D's infrared photoreceptors had locked onto Yoda, the Jedi Master's lightsaber was activated. Yoda's first swipe passed through the X10-D's legs, and his second neatly removed the droid's head from its shoulders.

Chief Scientist Frexton fainted. Yoda tried to revive him, hoping to learn what had happened to Teela Panjarra. But the man was out cold.

Yoda turned to the fallen body of the X10-D and knelt over its torso. He opened a panel on the droid's chest, only to discover the droid did not contain a plasma bomb.

Yoda wondered where the sixth X10-D could be.

Suddenly, bright overhead lights came on, illuminating the entire aeronautics laboratory. Ten meters away from Yoda, the LOCC lay on the lab floor. An X10-D draft droid had one foot firmly planted on top of the conveyor. Three Bartokk assassins were also in the lab. One Bartokk operated the remote-control device for the X10-D while the other two aimed crossbows loaded with explosive-tipped arrows at Yoda's heart.

The Jedi Master had walked right into the Bartokks' trap.

CHAPTER NINE

One of the crossbow-wielding Bartokks wore a vocabulator. Clicking its mandibles, the Bartokk cautioned, "If you make any sudden movement, we will make the droid crush the container and its contents."

Yoda did not move. He knew the Bartokk was serious.

"Our brothers on Level fifty-eight telepathically warned us of your position before they perished," the Bartokk continued. "We anticipated you would try to escape the tower, so we programmed all lifts to stop on this level. You have meddled with our assignment for the last time."

"Clever, you are," Yoda allowed. His mind raced, trying to plan his next move. Hoping to buy time, he added, "Detonate the plasma bomb, and perish too, you will."

The vocabulator-equipped Bartokk tilted his insectoid head toward a long, dart-shaped repulsorlift skiff parked next to a transport hatch. "We will leave the Science Service tower in our skiff and return to our starship. There is no place for you to run, warrior. We've sealed off this entire laboratory. We intend to leave you trapped within the tower. By the time the bomb detonates, we will be far away from Curamelle. Now you will remove your weapons."

Yoda reached to his belt and removed his lightsaber. With incomprehensible speed, he activated the lightsaber and flung it at the Bartokk who controlled the X10-D. Using the Force, Yoda guided his weapon through the air, slicing through both the Bartokk and his remote-control device, then curving back around. As the X10-D fell back against his controller, Yoda caught the lightsaber by its polished handle and spun at the two crossbow-wielding Bartokks.

The Bartokks fired their explosive-tipped arrows at Yoda. The Jedi Master's lightsaber flicked out at the oncoming bolts, snapping them in half. The arrow tips struck the lab walls and exploded. Before the assassins could reload their crossbows, Yoda surged forward and defeated them.

The three Bartokks and the two X10-D draft droids lay motionless on the floor under the bright lights of the aeronautics lab. Nearby, the unconscious Chief Scientist Frexton remained stretched out on the spot where he had fainted.

Yoda went to the LOCC and looked through its small viewport. Miraculously, Teela Panjarra remained sound asleep, and wore a faint smile on her lips.

Yoda stepped away from the LOCC and went to the sixth X10-D. Opening its chest plate, he found what he had expected: the third plasma bomb. As he carefully removed the bomb from the droid, he saw the Bartokks had taken an extreme precaution to prevent him from deactivating the explosive device.

Unlike the other two plasma bombs, the third bomb had a secured timer mechanism that had been set for a five-minute countdown. Any attempt to switch off the secured timer would cause the bomb to explode.

Since Bartokks communicate telepathically, Yoda figured that the four surviving members of the hive were aware they had lost the three Bartokks in the aeronautics lab. Unless the other four were in the Science Service tower, nothing would prevent the remaining Bartokks from leaving Corulag.

Yoda realized he was the only one who could get rid of the bomb and stop the Bartokks. Although it would be a dangerous mission, he dared not leave Teela Panjarra alone and undefended in the tower. He reluctantly decided to take the LOCC with him as well as the plasma bomb.

Yoda placed the LOCC and bomb on the Bartokks' skiff and gripped the vehicle's controls. He fired the skiff's engines, and the dart-shaped vessel blasted out of the aeronautics lab transport hatch.

The skiff soared away from the pyramidal Science Service tower. Yoda steered around the tower to locate the stolen SoroSuub space yacht.

The lights of Curamelle seemed to flow past the skiff like an illuminated wave. Searching for the space yacht, Yoda angled toward the low-rise buildings across from the tower's nursery window on Level 7.

Then he saw it. The SoroSuub space yacht was already rising up and away from its hiding place. Yoda swung the skiff after the space yacht, drawing closer until he was within thirty meters of it. Unfortunately, the assassins had anticipated his pursuit.

A Bartokk appeared on the stern of the space yacht and aimed a disrupter rifle at Yoda. The energy weapon was capable of unleashing a blast so powerful that it could break down targets at the molecular level. The Bartokk fired, and Yoda swung hard and away to avoid the energy blast. Yoda brought the skiff into a tight spin that positioned him directly under the fleeing space yacht, then came up toward the yacht's stern and punched the accelerator.

The nose of the skiff caught the Bartokk's skull. The disrupter rifle flew from his claws and skittered across the deck, while the Bartokk himself was knocked clear off the yacht.

Yoda matched the SoroSuub space yacht's speed, then landed the skiff on the yacht's open stern. He intended to plant the plasma bomb on the space yacht, then escape the stolen craft. Although there were barely two minutes left before the plasma bomb was set to detonate, Yoda wanted to be certain there weren't any innocent people on board.

He left Teela Panjarra within her LOCC, then carried the geodesic plasma bomb away from the skiff and crossed the yacht's aft deck.

Yoda walked past a supply bulkhead and a hatch for an emergency escape pod, then stepped up to the base of a curved, tubular air vent and peered through a viewport into the main cabin. Inside the cabin, three Bartokks operated the controls of the sleek vessel. They appeared to be unaware of Yoda's presence on the yacht.

Yoda tossed the bomb into the tubular air vent, then scurried back across the deck and onto the skiff. As he prepared for launch, he sensed something was wrong. He looked for Teela Panjarra's conveyor, and discovered it was missing.

Without warning, the yacht's canopy shields rose swiftly and sealed off the stern. Yoda heard a chittering sound from the deck that caused him to turn.

The Bartokk Queen stood on the deck. She was tall for a Bartokk, and her insectoid limbs displayed strong, flat muscles. Yoda realized there could be only one explanation for her presence on the yacht: She must have decided to personally oversee the ill-fated assignment to Corulag. Except for a handheld vocabulator, the Queen did not appear to be carrying any weapons. In the Queen's lower left claw, she carried Teela Panjarra's LOCC.

The Queen raised the vocabulator to her bulbous-eyed head and rasped, "Prepare to die, warrior."

"On this yacht, a plasma bomb is," Yoda replied as he stepped away from the skiff. He walked toward the guardrail, under which lay the fallen disrupter rifle. "Requires time, fighting does. Time you have not. Surrender the child, you will."

The Bartokk Queen laughed. "Foolish warrior," she snarled. "For failing our mission, we are prepared to die. You, on the other hand, have only managed to lock yourself up with us." The Queen extended her arm and crushed the vocabulator in her claw. Then she opened her claw, letting the broken bits fall to the stern's highly polished deck. She released the LOCC, letting it land with a dull thud on the deck. With all her claws free, the Queen assumed an attack position and prepared to strike.

Keeping his eyes on the Queen, Yoda slowly shook his head. "Not locked up with you, am I," he replied as he edged toward the guardrail. "Locked up with *me*, are you."

The Queen must have assumed Yoda was going to try using the disrupter rifle, and she pounced with her razor-sharp claws outstretched. She was still in midair when Yoda stepped away from the fallen rifle, activated his lightsaber, and let the Bartokk Queen fall upon its lethal blade.

The Queen was split in half and sprawled on the deck, but the two body parts rose quickly and tried to claw Yoda. The Jedi Master swung his lightsaber again and again, until there was little left of the Queen but flipping bits of insectoid armor.

Only the Queen's head remained intact. It rested on its side on the deck, looking at the remains of her body.

The SoroSuub space yacht veered off course, and the three surviving Bartokks stepped out of the main cabin. Teela Panjarra's conveyor began to slide across the deck toward the cabin, but Yoda grabbed hold of it. By Yoda's calculation, the plasma bomb would detonate in less than twenty seconds.

Yoda pushed and followed Teela Panjarra's LOCC into the yacht's emergency escape pod. The moment they were inside the cushioned confines of the pod, Yoda hit the ejection button.

The pod blasted out and zoomed away from the SoroSuub space yacht. Anticipating the blast, Yoda placed a protective hand over the viewport on Teela Panjarra's LOCC while he closed his own eyes. The pod was suddenly rocked by an incredible explosion, followed by a thunderous boom. The plasma bomb had detonated on schedule. Even with his eyes shut, Yoda could see the intense light of the massive explosion.

The shock wave subsided, and the pod descended to the Science Service tower. Yoda opened the LOCC to check on Teela Panjarra. She yawned, opened her eyes, looked at Yoda . . .

. . . and giggled.

At this point, readers who chose to follow the adventure in the Star Wars Adventures Game Book can return to *Jedi Emergency.*

CHAPTER TEN

Qui-Gon Jinn and Obi-Wan Kenobi watched as Chief Scientist Frexton was led away from the Science Service tower by the Academy Security Police. Nearby, the President of the Academy himself was assuring Mace Windu and Yoda that Frexton would never set foot in a laboratory again.

"It's most fortunate that no harm came to Teela Panjarra," Qui-Gon noted.

"Not to mention the entire Academy," Obi-Wan added.

Yoda and Mace Windu turned away from the Academy's President and approached Qui-Gon and Obi-Wan. The infant Teela Panjarra was cradled in Yoda's arms.

Qui-Gon's comlink chirped. He removed the device from his belt, held it in front of his face, and said, "Yes?"

From the comlink, Vel Ardox's voice answered, "The *Radiant VII* is ready to transport us all back to Coruscant whenever you're ready."

Qui-Gon smiled as he responded. "We're on our way back to Docking Bay thirty-nine-G now."

On the tarmac of Docking Bay 39-G, Bama Vook and Leeper stood beside the *Metron Burner* and waved as the *Radiant VII* lifted off. Bama and Leeper had figured that as long as they were on Corulag, they might try and drum up some business to run a shipment back to Esseles.

The Jedi were transporting Teela Panjarra back to the Jedi Temple. While Mace Windu received a HoloNet message from Coruscant, the other Jedi waited for him in the *Radiant VII*'s conference room. Qui-Gon was engaged in conversation with Vel Ardox and Noro Zak, and Obi-Wan turned to Adi Gallia and said, "There's something I've been meaning to ask you, Master Adi."

"Yes, Obi-Wan?"

"Master Qui-Gon has told me that you saved his life last year, but he has not told me the details. I thought perhaps you might tell me of the incident."

Adi Gallia looked confused, and turned to Obi-Wan's Master. "Qui-Gon? What's this about me saving your life last year?"

"Remember the official banquet for the Hewett senators?" Qui-Gon asked. "You stopped me before I took a bite of Konkeel pie."

"What?" Obi-Wan exclaimed. "You mean . . . Master Adi simply prevented you from eating dessert?"

"Konkeel pie is highly toxic to humanoids," Adi Gallia stated. "The Hewett senators apologized and removed it from their menu."

Qui-Gon looked at Obi-Wan and remarked, "People *have* died from eating it."

"Oh," said Obi-Wan.

Mace Windu entered the conference room. "I've

received a message from Chancellor Valorum," Mace Windu informed the gathered Jedi. "The matter of the Trade Federation constructing droid starfighters in the Darpa Sector is under investigation. The Trade Federation representatives, of course, deny any wrongdoing."

"We'll have to keep a very watchful eye on the Neimoidians," Qui-Gon said.

Obi-Wan looked to Qui-Gon and asked, "Master? Do you think we'll ever find out who hired the Bartokks to attack Corulag?"

Qui-Gon shook his head. "The answer to that question may have died with the Bartokks."

After Groodo the Hutt and his son Boonda saw the explosion high in the sky over Curamelle city, they realized the Bartokks had failed their assignment to destroy Corulag Academy. Groodo bitterly swore he'd never do business with Bartokk assassins again. Boonda kept his mouth shut. In truth, Boonda hadn't really wanted to go to the Academy anyway. He thought the Academy had too many rules.

Groodo couldn't wait to leave Corulag and return to Esseles. The two Hutts abandoned their escape pod and slowly made their way to the Academy Spaceport. They were slithering past Docking Bay 39-G when Boonda tugged at the flab of his father's left elbow.

"Look, pa," Boonda said, pointing at the Corellian freighter inside the docking bay. "That's Bama Vook's starship. I know him from Esseles. He's the test pilot for Trinkatta Starships."

"Really?" Groodo replied, beaming. "We must hire him to deliver us to Esseles at once."

"I can't wait to tell the gang back home about our adventure on Corulag!" young Boonda exclaimed.

"Boonda," Groodo growled, "let's just keep all that to ourselves."

NEXT ADVENTURE: THE GHOSTLING CHILDREN